Dear Parents,

Welcome to the Magic School Bus!

For over 20 years, teachers, parents, and children have been enchanted and inspired by Ms. Frizzle and the fabulous cast of beloved characters that make up The Magic School Bus series.

The unusual field trips, visual jokes, eye-catching details, and interesting information are just a few of the elements that make The Magic School Bus series an excellent tool to get your child excited about school, reading, and exploring their world.

It is important that children learn to read well enough to succeed in school and beyond. Here are some ideas for reading this book with your child:

- Look at the book together. Encourage your child to read the title and make a prediction about the story.
- Read the book together. Encourage your child to sound out words when appropriate. When your child struggles, you can help by providing the word.
- Encourage your child to retell the story. This is a great way to check for comprehension.

Enjoy the experience of helping your child learn to read and love to read!

Visit www.scholastic.com/magicschoolbus to subscribe to Scholastic's free parent e-newsletter, and find book lists, read-aloud tips, and learning hints for pre-readers, beginners, and older kids, too. Inspire a love of books in your child!

There are many Magic School Bus books for your reader to enjoy. We think you will enjoy these, too:

Ms. Frizzle

Liz

Written by Kristin Earhart
Illustrated by Carolyn Bracken

Based on The Magic School Bus® books
written by Joanna Cole and illustrated by Bruce Degen

The author and editor would like to thank Jonathan D. W. Kahl, Professor
of Atmospheric Science at the University of Wisconsin-Milwaukee, for
his expert advice in preparing the manuscript and illustrations.

ISBN-13: 978-0-545-08603-5
ISBN-10: 0-545-08603-5

12 11 10 9 8 7 6 5 4   10 11 12 13 14/0

Designed by Rick DeMonico
First printing, October 2008
Printed in the U.S.A.   40

The Magic School Bus®
Weathers the Storm

Arnold   Ralphie   Keesha   Phoebe   Carlos   Tim   Wanda   Dorothy Ann

Cartwheel
·B·O·O·K·S·®

SCHOLASTIC INC.

New York   Toronto   London   Auckland   Sydney
Mexico City   New Delhi   Hong Kong   Buenos Aires

It's fun to be in Ms. Frizzle's class.
She wears funny clothes and funny shoes.
We go on trips in the Magic School Bus.

HAIL STORM
Carlos

HURRICAN
D.A

TORNADO
Ralphie

RAIN CHART

DAY	INCHES OF RAIN
MON.	0″
TUES.	0″
WED.	

We are learning about weather.
Tim made a rain gauge.
It tells how much rain comes down.
But today it is empty.

RAIN CHART

DAY	INCHES OF RAIN
MON.	0"
TUES.	0"
WED.	0"

I WISH IT WOULD RAIN.

I DON'T. WE CAN'T PLAY BALL IN THE RAIN.

WHO WANTS TO PLAY BALL IN THIS HEAT?

The air is hot and sticky.
We all feel lazy and grumpy.
The Friz takes one look at us
and says, "Time for a field trip!"

Outside, it is still hot and sticky.
But the sky is clear blue.
"It is not going to rain," Keesha says to Tim.

LOOK, THERE ARE NO CLOUDS.

9

Ms. Frizzle drives to a lake.
Ms. Frizzle drives *into* the lake.
The bus changes into a boat.

NOT AGAIN!

We start to change, too.

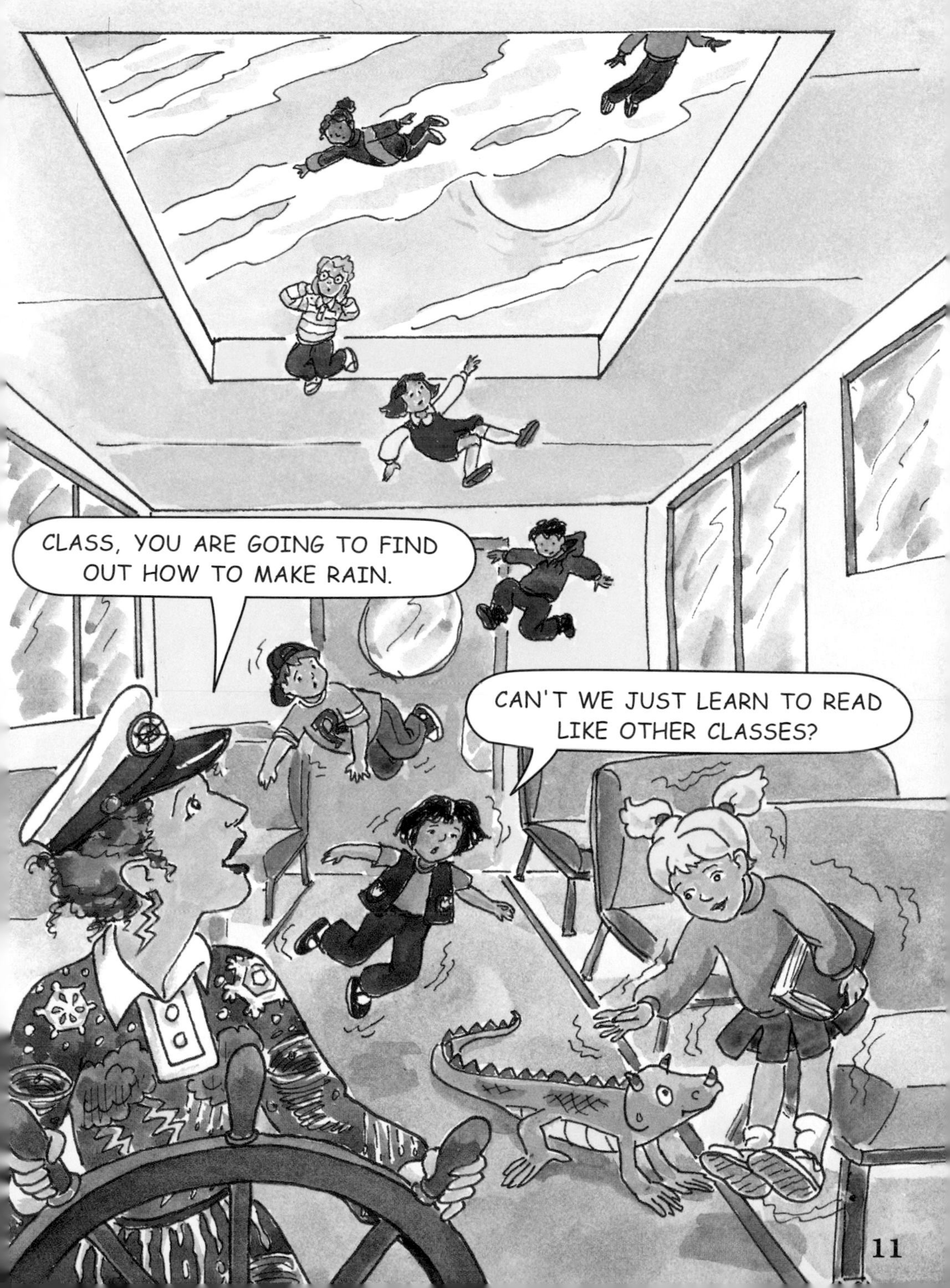

13

15

19

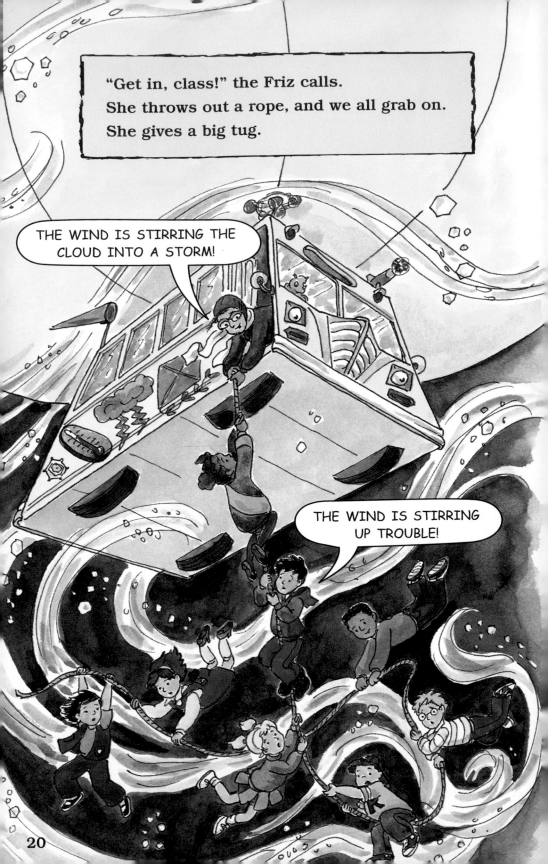

"Get in, class!" the Friz calls.
She throws out a rope, and we all grab on.
She gives a big tug.

We are safe in the weather balloon.
The balloon drops lower in the cloud.
There is a funny feeling in the air.

KIDS, WE ARE GOING TO SEE SOME FLASHY WEATHER!

I LIKE BORING WEATHER. AND BORING CLASS TRIPS.

THE SHAPE OF A STORM CLOUD

Just then, we see a bolt zip toward the ground.
It is a bolt of lightning!
"Lightning is full of energy," the Friz says.
"It makes light, heat, and a lot of sound."

Suddenly, the floor falls from the weather balloon! We tumble out.

25

After our raindrops land,
we hear a loud honk.
All at once, we are on the bus.

29

Wild Weather Facts

The largest hailstone was found in Aurora, Nebraska, on June 22, 2003. It was 7 inches wide — bigger than a cantaloupe!

Florida gets over 100 thunderstorms a year.

The Empire State Building is struck by lightning about 100 times each year. A lightning rod protects the building by controlling the lightning, heat, and energy.

A big thunderstorm can make enough electrical energy to light all the lights in a small town — even at the school!

CARLOS'S FORECAST FOR HUMOR

WHEN DO YOU KNOW IT IS RAINING CATS AND DOGS?

WHEN YOU STEP IN A POODLE!